My Journey from Bud to Boss

A Guide to Navigating the Transition to Remarkable Leadership

An Application and Learning Guide

Kevin Eikenberry

Guy Harris

Sara Jane Hope

My Journey from Bud to Boss: A Guide to Navigating the Transition to Remarkable Leadership

ISBN: 978-1-940485-00-3
LCCN: 2015902058

Interior book design, editing, and production: Jan Gilbert Hurst, Author's Voice Publishing, McPherson, Kansas
Printed in the United States of America

FIRST EDITION
10 9 8 7 6 5 4 3 2

Testimonials for *The Journey from Bud to Boss:*

"One of the great challenges of becoming a new boss is absorbing all the learning that you encounter as you prepare for the new job and a new role. Now *My Journey From Bud to Boss: A Guide to Navigating the Transition to Remarkable Leadership* makes that transition easy. With this step-by-step guide, a new supervisor can plan and chart his/her development in real-world action steps. Becoming a boss is never easy, but this new book will help the "journey" become more practical...and rewarding."

—John Baldoni, executive coach and author of *MOXIE: The Secret to Bold and Gutsy Leadership* and *Lead with Purpose*

"When I read, I highlight the daylights out of a book with all the things I plan to do with my new ideas. Shamefully, I rarely do any of them. There's no transfer from Good Idea to Implementation. This workbook contains a detailed, action filled self-study for you to translate the valuable *From Bud to Boss* book into action and results. It's not just about your Buds. As a leader, this workbook provides the tools to improve the whole dynamic including you, your team and your internal and external customers. Powerful templates show you and your team how to improve coaching, communication, influence and conflict resolution. Enough said—I have to leave and go all the way through this myself to grow my company."

—Lou Russell, CEO/Queen Russell Martin & Associates

"A great follow-up to the Bud to Boss Workshop! This isn't just for new readers or supervisors coming through the ranks. The material applies to many positions in the organization including seasoned managers that have been in their positions for years. Sometimes we forget how different 'Management' and 'Leadership' is...many of us are great Managers but few of us are great Leaders. This will definitely help you become a better Leader!"

—Jay DiSalvo, production manager, Durez Canada Company Ltd.

"Do you want to be a better leader? Read this new guide and you will be. It is chock-full of practical, effective, and thought-provoking activities...all designed to increase your effectiveness as a leader. Whether or not you've already read *From Bud to Boss*—and I hope you have—your confidence as a leader will grow by putting this wonderful guide to good use."

—Bill Treasurer, founder, Giant Leap Consulting and author of *Leaders Open Doors*

"*My Journey from Bud-to-Boss* is a great accompaniment to either *From Bud-to-Boss* book or the workshop. I look at it as an extension of the Personal Action Plan that is a part of the workshop. It makes you think of your strengths and weaknesses that you need to work on and commit them to Journey; used wisely, it will help you grow as a leader."

—May Leng Yuen

Acknowledgements

From Kevin . . .

A project like this is more than just the pages you are about to read and use. So many people have fingerprints here and to acknowledge them all would be nearly impossible. Instead, I will thank groups of people, including: the team at Wiley for producing the original *From Bud to Boss* book, the entire rock-star team at The Kevin Eikenberry Group, our trainers out working with leaders like you, all of our clients and workshop participants who made this book better, my co-authors Sara Jane and Guy—for without them it wouldn't have been completed, my family for their love and support, and mostly I thank God for the opportunity to use my talents to help others be more effective and successful.

From Guy . . .

I would like to thank the many Bud to Boss Workshop participants who have asked difficult questions and pushed for answers that helped me to think more deeply and critically about the difficult transition from "Bud to Boss." I would also like to thank my colleagues and friends at The Kevin Eikenberry Group who take care of the many administrative, marketing, sales, and logistics details that allow me to do what I do. And, I want to thank my wife, Sandra, for her patience and support as I work and write at odd hours of the day and night and travel from city to city to work with our clients and workshop participants.

From Sara Jane . . .

I appreciate the Kevin Eikenberry Group for giving me the opportunity to participate in the project of bringing the "Journey" to life. I would like to thank the trainers at Agrium in Soda Springs, Idaho, for understanding that training does not end when the classroom door closes and that a tool to continue the training process was needed. Asking for help in applying the lessons of "Bud to Boss" prompted the completion of the first draft and pilot use of this learning guide. Special thanks go to my husband, Larry, and all my family and friends who always are supportive of my endeavors.

We would all like to thank Jan Hurst, our designer and editor. Her patience and expertise made this product better in every way.

Contents

Introduction

If you are reading this, you have probably attended a Bud to Boss Workshop, are reading *From Bud to Boss*, or have read it. It is also highly probable that you have just been promoted to supervisor, hope to become a supervisor soon, or are looking for some assistance to improve your supervisory and leadership skills.

No matter what the reason, this book will be like a trusted assistant on your journey. (While having a copy of *From Bud to Boss* isn't critical, this book is written as a companion to it, and the value you will gain from this book will be enhanced with a copy.) Included here are activities, questions, and exercises designed to take you beyond the concepts introduced to you during the Workshop or the book. Each section covers a separate topic and each one is independent of the others. You can work through everything or work through only the sections where you need help at any given time. If we have done our job you will return to this companion often.

Remember that this guide is for you to complete and use at your own pace in your own way. The key to successfully using it is to answer the questions honestly and as completely as possible. This was designed as a workbook for you to write in, refer to, and use in the ways that work best for you.

Regardless of how you use it, we do hope that you will use it; because you, your team, and your organization deserve your best.

—Kevin, Guy, and Sara Jane

> There are many additional tools and templates referenced throughout this book. To access those tools, start by registering for the Bud to Boss Community at budtobosscommunity.com/my-journey-registration

How to Get the Most from This Book

Before you dive into this book, let's talk about how it can be most useful to you.

For starters, it isn't really a book. We know it looks (mostly) like a book. But since our childhood days of reading Dr. Seuss, we have "known" that a book is something you pick up and read—typically front to back. In that way, what you are holding is neither of those things. It isn't designed simply to be read—one glimpse ahead will show you that there are more places for you to write than there are words for you to read. And front to back isn't quite right either. While we have attempted to arrange the sections in an order that might be helpful if you are just starting as a supervisor or leader, your concerns might develop in a different order than how we have structured the book. Feel free to go through the sections in the order that best fit you and your situation— you will know what you need and when.

While you really can start anywhere, we do hope you do the first section—Are You Ready?—first. This section will help you directly in many ways as a supervisor and it will help you to make this tool most helpful as well.

We hope that you will consider this book as your companion on your Journey to becoming a more effective and confident leader. Yes, it is a companion volume to the *From Bud to Boss* book, and it can be a great companion to follow your attendance in one of our workshops. It is also more than that. It is your companion. Throughout the process of creating this book, all the way from concept to completion, we saw it and talked about it more as a journal and a resource than as a traditional book.

Given that more clearly defined picture of what you hold in your hands, use this in the way that works best for you.

In each section you will find:

Now Steps are specific actions you can take to help you through a particular leadership situation or help you answer a specific question you might have. Some are a bit more reflective and some are designed more for immediate use by you and/or your team, but all are meant to be used. In every case there is space for you to write in this book. Please write in this book! (If you don't usually write in books, you have permission. Remember, it isn't really a book anyway.) In many cases you have access to additional, downloadable copies of the forms and templates online so you can use them again and again in the future.

Next Steps close each section and give you longer-term thoughts on your development as a leader in this area of your role and responsibilities.

Throughout the Journey you will see references to additional tools and templates that are available to you online. You will want to take advantage of those resources. Gaining free access to all of them starts by registering for the Bud to Boss Community at:
www.budtobosscommunity.com/my-journey-registration/

If you have questions or comments or need additional help, please let us know by filling out the form at:
www.budtobosscommunity.com/contact-us/

With this said, we wish you great success. And we hope this "book" is a part of that success.

1
Are You Ready?

Which of the statements below best describes you?

- ❏ You are working to develop your skills so that you may be selected or promoted to supervisor.
- ❏ You recently applied for a supervisory position and you were selected.
- ❏ You recently applied for a supervisory position and you were not selected.
- ❏ You recently were promoted to a supervisory position because you have the longest tenure on your team.
- ❏ You recently were promoted to a supervisory position because you are considered to have the best technical skills.
- ❏ You have been in a supervisory position for six months or longer and have had some difficulties making the transition.
- ❏ You have been in a supervisory position for six months or longer and the transition has been smooth.
- ❏ You have been in a supervisory position for several years and it has been a successful and rewarding experience.
- ❏ You have been in a supervisory position for several years and it has been the most difficult thing you have ever experienced.

Regardless of which statement best describes you, you likely already realize that it takes a different set of skills and abilities to be a successful supervisor than an individual contributor. And, if you are like most people, you want to know how your skills and abilities rank with the skills of those who have become successful supervisors.

The truth is that there isn't an "ideal" or "model' to measure yourself against to assess whether or not you have what it takes. Many different types of individuals with a variety of skills and experiences have become successful supervisors. Yes, there are assessments you can take. Yes, there are tests which can rate your competency level with the competency level of others. None of these will guarantee that you will or will not be a successful supervisor.

There are mind-sets, attitudes, and ways of thinking about your new role and what it demands of you that will impact whether or not you will be successful. There are assessments that can help you make a determination as to whether or not you have a mind-set that is appropriate for success as a supervisor. Becoming aware of your own feelings about key areas that are related to being a supervisor as opposed to being an individual contributor may help you decide whether being a supervisor is really a role you wish to pursue.

In Kevin's book, *Remarkable Leadership*, he identified thirteen competencies that are needed to become a highly effective leader. That book, as well as *From Bud to Boss*, focuses on developing an individual's potential in those competency areas. Both of those books contain self-assessments to help you determine your potential for effectiveness in each competency area. *From Bud to Boss* and the Bud to Boss Workshop focus on five of the thirteen competencies. This Learning Guide also will also focus on those five competencies.

Activity 1: A Starting Self Assessment

❶ Complete the following assessments, which also appear at the beginning of each section (Parts I–VI) of *From Bud to Boss*.

Use the following scale of 1 to 7 to indicate the one that best describes you in response to the statements below.

1 Almost never
2 Rarely or seldom
3 Occasionally
4 Sometimes
5 Usually
6 Frequently
7 Almost always

Championing Change

1. I am comfortable with change personally. _____

2. I understand how change happens and what contributes to it. _____

3. I am able to successfully influence others to make changes and try new things. _____

4. I know what to do when change is forced upon me. _____

5. I am comfortable with my role in communicating change. _____

6. I am able to recognize and overcome resistance to change in myself and others. _____

Communicating Powerfully

1. I use a communication model to help me communicate more clearly. _____

2. I know how to describe common behavioral traits in an objective way. _____

3. I can clearly see and use the dynamics of interactions between people. _____

4. I know how to create an environment that meets the needs of people on my team. _____

5. I know how to adjust my communication style to better connect with others. _____

6. I communicate in powerful, persuasive, and memorable ways. _____

Developing Others (Coaching)

1. I am comfortable with my ability to give feedback that will be well received. _____

2. I am confident in my ability to coach and develop others. _____

3. I am comfortable in receiving feedback from others. _____

4. I can successfully lead performance reviews. _____

5. I am supportive of those I lead. _____

Valuing Collaboration and Teamwork

1. I know what to do to make my team meetings productive. _____

2. I understand my role as team leader in meetings. _____

3. I know how to accurately and objectively assess my team's performance. _____

4. I know how to help my team achieve success as a team. _____

5. I understand how conflicts start and escalate. _____

6. I know what to do to stop conflict escalation. _____

Setting Goals and Supporting Goal Setting

1. I consider myself a successful goal achiever. _____

2. I regularly set goals. _____

3. I am confident in my ability to help others set goals. _____

4. I know my role in helping my team achieve their goals. _____

5. I have a positive attitude at work and in life in general. _____

6. I provide support and focus to help my team achieve their goals.

_____

❷ Review your responses to your assessments. On the lines below, list the sections where more than half of your responses are 4 or less. These are likely your weaknesses as a leader.

_____

_____

_____

_____

_____

_____

❸ On the lines below, list the areas of your responses where more than half of your responses are 5 or above. These are likely your strengths as a leader.

_____

_____

_____

_____

_____

_____

YOUR **NEXT** STEPS

Here are some suggestions for actions you may take after completing the assessments and identifying key strengths or weaknesses:

1 Start with the sections in this book on your areas of weakness.

2 Look through your notes from the Bud to Boss Workshop on the subject, if applicable.

3 Read the section of *From Bud to Boss* which covers the subject.

4 Read the chapter in *Remarkable Leadership* which covers the subject.

5 Go to **www.budtobosscommunity.com** and access the accompanying Bonus Bytes.

6 Repeat these steps for your areas of greatest strength.

Suggested Reading

Eikenberry, Kevin. *Remarkable Leadership*. Jossey-Bass, 2007.

Fritz, Roger. *Think Like a Manager*. Career Press, 2001.

Haneberg, Lisa. *10 Steps to Be a Successful Manager*. ASTD, 2007.

Kouzes, James M., and Barry Z. Posner. *The Leadership Challenge*. John Wiley & Sons, 2012.

Maxwell, John C. *The 21 Irrefutable Laws of Leadership*. Thomas Nelson, Inc., 2007.

Additional Notes

2
How Different Will It Be?

You probably already have given a lot of thought to what will be different for you as a supervisor. This section will take a closer look at some of the changes you may encounter and help you consider ways that you can make the transition to your new role easier.

Activity 1: Your New Tasks and Responsibilities

1 What do you think will change in your duties and responsibilities when you become a supervisor?

☞ What do you "know" from conversations and your job description?

☞ What are your additional assumptions?

❷ What new tasks will be added to your daily, weekly, or yearly schedule?

    ✎ What new tasks do you currently have the knowledge, skills, and abilities needed to complete successfully?

    ✎ Which of these new tasks will require you to improve your knowledge, skills, and abilities?

❸ What new tasks are completely unfamiliar?

    ✎ What steps will you take to learn these tasks?

4 Who/what are the resources available to you? List them below:

Task or Skill	Resource

5 What is the relative priority for learning these knowledge, skill, and ability areas?

✎ Has your supervisor given you any ideas here? Have you asked? If so, list them here.

6 What is your intended timeline for becoming competent in these new knowledge, skill, and ability areas?

Activity 2: Your Roles

❶ What new roles have been added to your work life? Consider this list of possible roles and check the ones that apply to you. Then rate your level of confidence in these roles on a scale from 1 to 10 (with 10 being the highest possible confidence).

Role	Apply to You?	Confidence Level
Decision Maker		
Performance Evaluator		
Team Leader		
Goal Setter		
Management Team Member		
Delegator		
Accountability Holder		
Project Manager		
Meeting Facilitator		
Budget Preparer		
Conflict Resolver		
Vendor Contact		
Trainer		
Assignment Giver		
Problem Solver		
Innovator		
Other		

❷ What steps will you take to learn the skills and responsibilities associated with these roles?

❸ Who/what can serve as a resource to help you learn the needed skills and responsibilities?

Skill Area	Resource

Activity 3: Your Changing Relationships

❶ Which relationships in your work life will change?

Name	Role

❷ How will your relationships with those people change?

Activity 4: Your New Relationships

Use the table on the following page to complete this activity. Use additional space in the back of this book if necessary. To get a digital copy of this form, register for the Bud to Boss Community at **www.budtobosscommunity.com/my-journey-registration/**

❶ Column 1: List each person with whom you will have to develop a relationship.

❷ Column 2: Indicate the reason for the relationship and what needs to result from the relationship.

❸ Column 3: Identify the information that you need to know about this person that will assist you in developing your working relationship.

❹ Column 4: Describe the action steps you will take to develop a relationship with this person.

❶ Person	**❷ Reason/Result**	**❸ Information**	**❹ Action Steps**

Activity 5: Your Attitudes and Beliefs

1 What current attitudes and beliefs do you have that may affect your ability to lead/supervise others? Here are some examples to assist you in your thinking. Indicate whether you agree or disagree with each of the following statements:

Statement	Agree	Disagree
If something does not get done, it is my responsibility to do it.		
The people on my team are more motivated by their leisure activities than they are by their work accomplishments.		
I get frustrated when people question what I ask them to do.		
All good employees know what to do without being told or reminded.		
Most people are primarily motivated by money and status when it comes to workplace behaviors.		
The main reason people don't take responsibility or initiative is that they don't want to decide.		
It is my responsibility to remind and prod people towards accomplishment.		
My team members' suggestions and input have limited value because of their experience level and/or access to information.		

2 How can these attitudes and beliefs affect your ability to lead and supervise others? Are they useful or detrimental?

3 Do you need to adjust these attitudes and beliefs or adapt new ones in order to be more successful?

① Review this section after you have been in your supervisory position for several months.

② Determine how accurate you were in determining the changes needed in your transition to supervisor.

③ Evaluate whether or not you made these changes effectively:

☞ What parts of the transition went well?

☞ Why did these parts go well? What are your key lessons?

☞ What areas do you still need to complete?

Suggested Reading

Blanchard, Ken and Spencer Johnson. *The One-Minute Manager*. Harper-Collins, 1982.

Covey, Stephen R. *The 7 Habits of Highly Effective People*. Free Press, 2004.

Eikenberry, Kevin. *Remarkable Leadership*. Jossey-Bass, 2007.

Fritz, Roger. *Think Like a Manager*. Career Press, 2001.

Haneberg, Lisa. *10 Steps to Be a Successful Manager*. ASTD, 2007.

Tulgan, Bruce. *It's Okay to Be the Boss*. HarperCollins Publishers, 2007.

Watkins, Michael. *The First 90 Days: Proven Strategies for Getting Up to Speed Faster and Smarter*. Harvard Business Review Press, 2013.

Additional Notes

3
What Are My Expectations of Myself?

In your career, you have likely worked for different types of supervisors. There are ones who micromanage and watch over every step you take. There are those who rarely speak with you and let you do whatever you want to do as long as you reach your goals—or not. There are yellers and screamers. There are silent types. There are some who want to know everything about you and others who are aloof and may be seen as arrogant.

You get the picture. The bottom line is that you have many choices to make about the kind of supervisor you will be.

We want you to make conscious choices rather than act simply from habit or past experience. The exercises that follow will help you make these choices.

YOUR

Activity 1: Your Previous Supervisors

❶ Think about a great supervisor you have had—someone you would willingly help if they asked. What were their behaviors, attitudes, and/or actions? List your thoughts below...

Best Leader

_____

_____

_____

_____

_____

_____

_____

_____

✏ What focus did they have in their thinking? Whom do you think they considered first in their decisions?

❷ Now think about the other extreme—someone you would avoid completely or you would help only minimally. What were their behaviors, attitudes, and/or actions? List your thoughts below...

Worst Leader

_____

_____

_____

_____

_____

_____

_____

_____

_____

_____

✏ What focus did they have in their thinking? Whom do you think they considered first in their decisions?

❸ Now think about both leaders:

✏ How did you feel about the person you saw as the "Best Leader"?

✏ How did you feel about the person you saw as the "Worst Leader"?

✏ Did you grant them influence or did they demand it? Explain.

✏ How can you adopt the attitudes and perspectives of your "Best Leader"?

✏ What can you learn about leadership from your "Worst Leader"?

Activity 2: Your Working Style

❶ Consider your answers to the following questions:

✎ How much do you want to be involved in the day-to-day activities of each of your team members?

✎ What latitude will you give your team members in developing how they will complete their assignments?

✎ How often will you meet with each of your team members individually?

✎ How often will you meet with your entire team?

✏ What information do you want to know/have about each of your team members?

✏ What information do you want your team members to know/have about you?

✏ What expectations do you have of yourself in your role as supervisor?

Activity 3: Thinking About Myself

❶ Rate your level of agreement or disagreement with each of the following statements on a scale of 1–10, with 10 being "I completely agree" and 1 being "I fully disagree."

Statement	Rating
I expect to be liked by each of my team members.	
I believe that I will never make a mistake.	
I will admit to my supervisor that I have made a mistake.	
I will admit to my team that I have made a mistake.	
I feel that I know most of what I need to know to do my job.	
I will continue to learn new things.	
I will help others grow and develop.	
I will give feedback to others that will help them to do their jobs.	
I feel that I must make all of the decisions that impact my team.	
I must know how to do everything that my team members do.	

❷ Think about your responses to the following questions:

✏ What do the above statements say about your expectations of yourself as a supervisor?

✏ Are your expectations realistic?

✏ What steps will you take to live up to your expectations of yourself?

❸ Talk to your supervisor, a former supervisor, or a peer. Ask them how they perceive your attitude to the questions above.

✏ Discuss any differences in perspective with them.

✏ What did you learn from these discussions?

❹ Reflect on the perceptions others have of you that you would like to change. What are they?

❺ Identify your action steps to make these changes.

YOUR **NEXT** STEPS

❶ Review your answers to the above activities after you have been in the position for a few months.

❷ Evaluate how well you have lived up to your own expectations.

❸ Determine whether or not your attitudes about being a supervisor have changed.

❹ Consider whether or not you need to change any of your expectations of yourself in your supervisory role.

Suggested Reading

Buckingham, Marcus. *The One Thing You Need to Know*. Free Press, 2005.

Eikenberry, Kevin. *Remarkable Leadership*. Jossey-Bass, 2007.

Fritz, Roger. *Think Like a Manager*. Career Press, 2001.

Fulton, Roger V. *Common Sense Supervision*. Ten Speed Press, 1988.

Goldsmith, Marshall. *What Got You Here Won't Get You There*. Hyperion, 2010.

Haneberg, Lisa. *10 Steps to Be a Successful Manager*. ASTD, 2007.

Additional Notes

More Notes

4
What Are My Expectations of Others?

Here's a quick review of the Pygmalion Effect and the Galatea Effect:

1. **The Pygmalion Effect:** People tend to live up (or down) to your expectations of them.

2. **The Galatea Effect:** People who have positive expectations of themselves tend to perform better than people who have negative expectations.

You cannot control an individual's expectations of themselves. You can, however, influence them by your actions and interactions with them. Your word choice, tone, and body language communicate elements of your expectations of and belief in others. Your expectations and beliefs have such a strong impact that your team's performance tends to track with your expectations. In other words, if you have high expectations of and belief in others, there is a greater chance they will perform well. If you do not, more than likely they will not.

Activity 1: Team Member Strengths and Weaknesses

If your organization has a process or forms for completing the following activities, feel free to use the tools provided by your organization. If not (or you would like resources to support your organization's existing resources), use the forms we have provided below. You can get downloadable digital versions of these forms by registering for the Bud to Boss Community at **www.budtobosscommunity.com/my-journey-registration/**

Use the table on the following page to complete this activity. Use additional space in the back of this book if necessary.

❶ Column 1: List your team members.

❷ Column 2: Identify their strengths.

❸ Column 3: Identify areas for improvement.

❶ Team Member	❷ Strengths	❸ Opportunities for Improvement

Activity 2: Team Member Confidence

Use the table on the following page to complete this activity. Use additional space in the back of this book if necessary.

❶ Column 1: List your team members.

❷ Column 2: Rate what you feel is their current level of self-confidence on a scale of 1–10 (with 10 being excellent).

❸ Column 3: Rate how you feel they would rate their current level of performance on a scale of 1–10 (with 10 being excellent).

❹ Column 4: Identify steps you could take to increase each individual's level of self-confidence.

❺ Column 5: Identify steps (task assignments, goals, etc.) that would increase each individual's level of performance.

❶ Team Member	❷ Self-Confidence Rating	❸ Self-Performance Rating	❹ Self-Confidence Action Steps	❺ Performance Action Steps

Activity 3: Team Member Work

Use the following table to complete this activity. Additional forms can be downloaded after registering for the Bud to Boss Community at **www.budtobosscommunity.com/my-journey-registration/**

❶ Column 1: List each of your team members.

❷ Column 2: Identify the top 5 tasks/responsibilities of each team member.

❸ Column 3: Identify the top 5 result areas you expect from each team member.

❶ Team Member	❷ Top 5 Tasks/Responsibilities	❸ Top 5 Result Areas

4 Ask each of your team members to complete steps 2 and 3.

5 Meet and discuss the two lists to reconcile any differences between your thoughts and theirs, and to discuss action plans identified by the exercise.

6 Answer the following questions:

☞ How will you ensure that you and each team member agree on the top five tasks/responsibilities?

☞ How will you ensure that you and each team member agree on the key result areas for his/her position?

☞ How will you follow-up with each team member to determine if he/she is working on the priorities for his/her position?

Note: You can use the coaching model you read about in *From Bud to Boss* or learned in the Bud to Boss Workshop to have these conversations. The diagram on the next page describes this model.

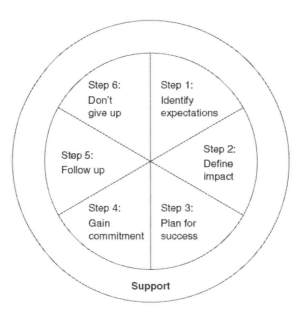

❶ Review your notes on the above activities after you have been in your supervisory role for a few months.

☞ How accurate were your opinions and perspectives of your team members?

☞ Have your team members lived up to the expectations that you set for them?

☞ How successfully did you complete the action steps you outlined to enhance your team members' self-confidence and their performance?

✏ How have your expectations of your team members changed now that you know them better?

❷ Plan ways you can influence your team members to continue improving their self-confidence and performance.

Suggested Reading

Buckingham, Marcus. *Go Put Your Strengths to Work*. Free Press, 2010.

Buckingham, Marcus and Donald Clifton. *Now, Discover Your Strengths*. Free Press, 2001.

Eikenberry, Kevin. *Remarkable Leadership*. Jossey-Bass, 2007.

Rath, Tom. *Strengths Finder*. Gallup Press, 2007.

Additional Notes

5
What Conversations Do I Need to Have?

In both the Bud to Boss Workshop and the *From Bud to Boss* book, Kevin and Guy recommended that you have transition conversations with key people in order to discuss the changes in your relationship and inter-actions. These conversations will help you understand more about their expectations of you, and you will communicate more about your expectations of them.

This section will help you plan these transition conversations.

There are many groups listed here—not all will apply to you. Time invested in those that do apply will pay big returns.

Conversation 1: Your New Boss

Before You Meet:

❶ Rate your relationship with your new boss on a scale of 1–10 (with 10 being excellent).

❷ Have you worked with this person before? If so, describe that relationship.

❸ Prepare a list of questions before you meet. Here are some suggestions (Make sure to ask those with an asterisk.)

 ✍ *What are the big keys for your success?

 ✍ *What do they most want you to accomplish?

 ✍ *What are their expectations of you?

 ✍ How do they want you to communicate with them?

- How often will you meet?

- What advice would they give you about leading your new team?

- Who (besides them) would they suggest that you ask to mentor or coach you?

- Why were you selected for the position?

- *What areas of improvement do they see for you?

- *What do they see as your strengths?

During the Meeting:

❶ Record the answers for your review and reflection later.

❷ Share what expectations you have of them. Do so respectfully, and yet clearly let them know what you'd like from them. For example...

- What are your communication preferences?

- How often would it be helpful for you to meet with them to discuss goals and results?

- What issues do you anticipate needing their help to address?

❸ Take additional notes.

Conversation 2: Individual Team Members

Before You Meet:

Use the table on the following page to prepare for these conversations. Additional forms can be downloaded after registering for the Bud to Boss Community at **www.budtobosscommunity.com/my-journey-registration/**

❶ Column 1: List the names of your team members.

❷ Column 2: List what you need to know about each of your team members.

❸ Column 3: Rate how you think this person feels about you on a scale of 1–10 (with 10 being a close trusting relationship).

❹ Column 4: List what you believe those feelings are based upon.

❺ Column 5: Indicate the boundaries/agreements that need to be established.

❻ After completing this table, meet with each person.

❶ Team Member	❷ What You Need to Know	❸ Rating of Their Feelings About You	❹ Feelings Based Upon	❺ Needed Boundaries/Agreements

During the Meeting:

❶ Discuss needed items plus anything they bring to the conversation.

❷ Ask what assistance they need from you.

❸ Ask questions like these:

✏ What are your concerns?

✏ What challenges do you face?

✏ What needs do you have?

✏ What questions do you have?

✏ What else do I need to know?

❹ Take additional notes.

Conversation 3: Your Whole Team

Before You Meet:

❶ List what you need to discuss with your team that applies to everyone. (Consider expectations, goals, team rules, etc. when making this list.)

During the Meeting:

❶ Discuss the items. Use their input as much as possible to establish the team expectations, goals, rules, etc.

❷ Ask them what they expect from you as a supervisor. (Listen, ask for clarity, and take notes!)

❸ Establish a plan for regular team meetings. (If you aren't sure how often to meet, build a tentative plan and adjust as needed in the future.)

❹ Take additional notes.

Conversation 4: Your Peers

Before You Meet:
Use the table on the following page to plan your conversations. Additional forms can be downloaded after registering for the Bud to Boss Community at **www.budtobosscommunity.com/my-journey-registration/**

❶ Column 1: List the members of your new peer group.

❷ Column 2: Describe the role/relationship you will have with the person in completing the tasks of your job.

❸ Column 3: Rate your current relationship with this person on a scale of 1–10 (with 10 being excellent).

❹ Column 4: Indicate what you need to know about this person and his/her role.

❺ Column 5: Describe what this person can do to help you learn your new role as supervisor.

❻ After completing this table, meet with each person.

❶ Peer	❷ Role/Relationship	❸ Rating of Current Relationship	❹ Need To Know	❺ How They Can Help

During the Meeting:

1 Ask what you can do to assist this person. Listen to their answers!

2 State what you need from them.

3 Determine ongoing or next steps with them.

4 Take notes.

Conversation 5: Your Former Boss

Before You Meet:

❶ Rate your current relationship with your former boss on a scale of 1–10 (with 10 being excellent).

❷ Will you continue to have a working relationship with your former boss? *If yes, then this is an important conversation.*

❸ List the questions you have for your former boss concerning their evaluation of your skills and abilities to be supervisor. Here are some examples:

   ✏ What do they consider your strengths?

   ✏ What do they consider your opportunities for improvement?

   ✏ Which of your existing skills do they see assisting you most as a supervisor?

✏ What do they suggest you work on first?

During the Meeting:

1 Ask the above questions and record their answers for later review and reflection.

2 Ask them for their advice for your new role. Record their answers for later review and reflection.

3 Take additional notes.

Conversation 6: Internal Customers

Before You Meet:

Use the table on the following page to prepare for these conversations. Additional forms can be downloaded after registering for the Bud to Boss Community at **www.budtobosscommunity.com/my-journey-registration/**

❶ Column 1: Make a list of your internal customers.

❷ Column 2: Describe what services/products you provide this customer.

❸ Column 3: Rate your current relationship with this customer on a scale of 1–10 (with 10 being excellent).

❹ Column 4: List any current issues/concerns that you know you have with this customer.

❺ Column 5: Identify actions you could take to improve or continue the current relationship.

❻ After completing this table, plan a regular meeting/communication schedule with this customer.

❶ Internal Customer	❷ Services/Products	❸ Rating of Current Relationship	❹ Current Issues/Concerns	❺ Actions Needed

Conversation 7: External Customers (If applicable)

Before You Meet:

Use the table on the following page to prepare for these conversations. Additional forms can be downloaded after registering for the Bud to Boss Community at **www.budtobosscommunity.com/my-journey-registration/**

❶ Column 1: Make a list of your external customers.

❷ Column 2: Describe what services/products you provide each customer.

❸ Column 3: Rate your current relationship with each customer on a scale of 1–10 (with 10 being excellent).

❹ Column 4: List current issues/concerns that you know you have with each customer.

❺ Column 5: Identify actions you could take to continue or improve current relationships.

❻ After completing this table, plan a regular meeting/communication schedule with each customer.

① External Customer	② Services/Products	③ Rating of Current Relationship	④ Current Issues/Concerns	⑤ Actions Needed

Conversation 8: Vendors *(If applicable)*

Before You Meet:

Use the table on the following page to prepare for these conversations. Additional forms can be downloaded after registering for the Bud to Boss Community at **www.budtobosscommunity.com/my-journey-registration/**

❶ Column 1: Make a list of your applicable vendors.

❷ Column 2: Describe what services/products each vendor provides to you.

❸ Column 3: Rate the current relationship with each vendor on a scale of 1–10 (with 10 being excellent).

❹ Column 4: List any current issues/concerns that you know you have with each vendor.

❺ Column 5: Identify actions you could take to continue or improve the current relationships.

❻ After completing this table, plan a regular meeting/communication schedule with each vendor.

❶ Vendors	❷ Services/Products	❸ Rating of Current Relationship	❹ Issues/Concerns	❺ Actions Needed

Conversation 9: Human Resources Representative
(If applicable)

Before You Meet:

❶ Rate your current knowledge of human resource policies and procedures (including employment laws) on a scale of 1–10 (with 10 being excellent).

❷ Determine which human resource representatives with whom you could consult.

❸ Ask about specific human resource policies and procedures that you need to become familiar with immediately.

❹ Determine how they (or others) can assist you with developing skills and knowledge in human resources policies and procedures.

❺ Establish a plan of action to develop the needed skills and knowledge.

Conversation 10: Union Steward/Representative
(if applicable)

1 Rate your current relationship with the union steward/representative on a scale of 1–10 (with 10 being excellent).

2 List the names of any union stewards/representatives with whom you need to establish a relationship to be highly successful.

3 Ask about specific information that you need to know and understand about the union contract and procedures.

4 Meet to discuss ways to work together successfully. Gain their perspective on the relationship. State your goal to have a productive and valuable relationship.

5 Establish a plan of action to develop your skills and knowledge regarding the union contract and relationships.

Activity 1: Family

This isn't a conversation, though your answers and reflections may lead to some. If that makes sense, we recommend you have those conversations, sooner rather than later!

❶ List what changes may occur in your personal/family life as a result of your new role or position.

❷ Determine and describe what kinds of boundaries you will set between your personal and work life.

❸ Determine how much your family members want to be involved or know about your issues at work.

❹ Plan the steps you will take to maintain the work/life balance you desire.

Activity 2: Self

All of us have that little voice in our heads that influences our beliefs about ourselves. Because of that voice, you need to establish positive thought patterns to enhance your self-confidence in your new role as supervisor.

❶ Identify your positive attributes that enhance your ability to be a successful supervisor.

❷ List the experiences you have had that will contribute to your role as a supervisor. Remember that both success and failure provide you with learning that can improve your current skills and abilities. This list may need more space. If so, please use additional space in the back of this book.

❸ Establish a procedure to review these positive attributes and experiences on a regular basis.

YOUR NEXT STEPS

❶ Review each of these relationships from time to time to see where you currently stand.

❷ Evaluate what parts of your original action plan you have completed and what still needs to be done.

❸ Consider what actions you can take to continually improve these relationships.

Suggested Reading

Eikenberry, Kevin. *Remarkable Leadership*. Jossey-Bass, 2007.

Patterson, Kerry and Al Switzler, Ron McMillan, Joseph Grenny, and Tom Peters. *Crucial Confrontations: Tools for Resolving Broken Promises, Violated Expectations, and Bad Behavior*. The McGraw-Hill Companies, 2004.

Patterson, Kerry, and Joseph Grenny, Ron McMillan, and Al Switzler. *Crucial Conversations: Tools for Talking When Stakes are High*. The McGraw-Hill Companies, 2011.

Scott, Susan. *Fierce Conversations: Achieving Success At Work and in Life One Conversation at a Time*. Penguin Group Incorporated, 2004.

Stone, Douglas, and Bruce Patton and Sheila Heen. *Difficult Conversations: How to Discuss What Matters Most*. Penguin Books, 2000.

6
How Well Do I Understand Others?

If you attended the Bud to Boss Workshop, you experienced an exercise and explanation of a behavior style model known as the DISC model of human behavior. If you have read *From Bud to Boss,* you read descriptions of the four main behavior styles and how the model is used. This model is a guide to understanding people and a tool for enhancing your communication with them.

Here's a quick review:

There are two basic drives for our behaviors:

1. **The Pace Drive:** how quickly or slowly we move through life, engage in activities, and make decisions.

2. **The Priority Drive:** which direction we tend to think most naturally in terms of task or people.

Combining the two drives with the strength of the tendency in each one results in four behavioral quadrants:

❑ **Dominant:** Outgoing and task oriented, focused on results and bottom-line discussion.

❑ **Inspiring:** Outgoing and people oriented, focused on interaction and friendly discussion.

❑ **Supportive:** Reserved and people oriented, focused on protecting relationships and collaborative discussion.

❑ **Cautious:** Reserved and task oriented, focused on excellence and data-driven discussion.

Refer to your Bud to Boss Learningbook or your *From Bud to Boss* book for a more extensive description of each of the quadrants. As you apply this model to working with your team members, remember that people are blends of these traits. Very few people have only one of the four traits present in their personal style blend.

Activity 1: Learn More About Your Style

❶ Go to www.DISCPersonalityTesting.com and click on the Free Assessment button to take a quick, free, behavior style assessment to better understand your style.

❷ Go to the Bonus Bytes page at **www.budtobosscommunity.com** and click on the Team Style button in the Communication Category for insights on how you can use the free assessment with your team.

Activity 2: Thinking About Your Team

Use the table on the following page to complete this activity. To get a digital copy of this form, register for the Bud to Boss Community at **www.budtobosscommunity.com/my-journey-registration/**

❶ Column 1: List each team member on your team.

❷ Column 2: Determine what you consider to be each person's primary behavior style based on the assessment or through personal observation and indicate it.

❸ Column 3: Consider how you may need to adapt your own behavior style to match that of each of your team members and record that.

❹ Column 4: Identify some specific things you may need to say or do with this person in order to communicate with and influence them more effectively.

❶ Team Member	**❷ Primary Style**	**❸ How to Adapt**	**❹ Action Steps**

5 After filling out the table, ask each team member for feedback on how you could communicate more effectively.

6 Reflect on the differences between your opinion and theirs.

1 Consider the Communicating for Results Workshop (**www.RemarkableCommunicator.com**) as the next step in your development.

2 Consider having your team members take the free assessment at **www.DISCPersonalityTesting.com** and share their report with you.

3 Meet with your team to explore how you could use your assessment results to work together more effectively. If you want help with this meeting, contact resources in your organization who are familiar with the DISC assessment or contact info@KevinEikenberry.com to get suggestions and help from us.

Suggested Reading

Carnegie, Dale. *How to Win Friends and Influence People.* Simon & Schuster, 2009.

Eikenberry, Kevin. *Remarkable Leadership.* Jossey-Bass, 2007.

Maxwell, John C. *Winning With People: Discover the People Principles That Work for You Every Time.* Thomas Nelson, Inc., 2007.

Ritchey, Tom and Alan Axelrod. *I'm Stuck, You're Stuck: Break Through to Better Work Relationships and Results By Discovering Your DiSC® Behavorial Style.* Berrett-Koehler Publishers, Inc., 2002.

Additional Notes

7
How Will I Communicate with Others?

Communication is not just about understanding someone's behavioral style. You must develop techniques for communicating in a clear and concise way and for listening so that you understand and can respond effectively to what is being said. One of the key decisions you will need to make as a supervisor is how and how often you will communicate with your team and what methods (media) you will use.

Activity 1: Learning From the Past

❶ Reflect on a time when a communication you had with someone went particularly well. Ask yourself:

✎ What did you specifically do during this conversation?

✎ How did you know that the communication was so successful?

☞ What aspects of the communication can you identify as being key to the success?

❷ Reflect on a time when your communication wasn't very effective. Ask yourself:

☞ What happened?

☞ What negatively impacted the results? (i.e., your words, tone, non-verbals, or something else?)

☞ What could you have said or done differently that might have improved the outcome?

☞ Did you have a follow-up conversation with the individual to discuss the miscommunication?

☞ If not, what might you gain from having a follow-up conversation? Meet with the person if you think it would be beneficial.

Activity 2: Gaining Perspective

❶ Schedule a conversation with your boss or one of your peers. Ask them to give you feedback on your communication effectiveness. Consider topics like those below and ask other questions to help you better understand.

✎ Ask about word choice.

- Is the vocabulary you use appropriate for your audience?
- Do you provide enough detail and specifics?
- Do you make false or unrealistic assumptions about how other people will interpret or understand what you say?

✎ Ask about your tone. Are you coming across the way you intended?

✎ Ask about your non-verbal messages. Do they match/support your verbal message?

Activity 3: Finding the Right Medium

❶ Think about the types of information you have to communicate and write a list in column 1 below.

❷ Indicate what you feel is the best method for communicating the information/topic. Choose from the following:

- ❑ Face-to-face group (team meeting)
- ❑ Face-to-face (individual)
- ❑ Phone/live chat
- ❑ Voice mail
- ❑ E-mail to a group
- ❑ E-mail to an individual
- ❑ Hard copy document—typed
- ❑ Hard copy document—hand written
- ❑ Instant message/text

❶ Type of Information	❷ Communication Method

YOUR **NEXT** STEPS

The exercise that follows is an effective tool for all communicators. It is a time investment with a high rate of return.

❶ Think about a conversation that you need to have with someone about an important matter. Plan for the conversation using these questions:

✏ What is the purpose/desired outcome?

✏ How will you open the conversation?

✏ What specific details will you share?

✏ What questions will you ask?

☞ How will you determine if the person understands your message?

☞ How will you ensure that you understand what the person is saying?

☞ How will you summarize?

☞ What is the most important thing you want to know as a result?

❷ Schedule the conversation and meet with the person.

❸ After the conversation reflect and then ask yourself questions like:

✏ Was the purpose of the conversation achieved?

✏ How did you feel after the conversation was completed?

✏ What action will you take to evaluate whether the conversation was effective?

✏ What would you do differently next time?

Suggested Reading

Allessandra, Tony and Phillip L. Hunsaker. *Communicating At Work.* Touchtone, 1993.

Booher, Dianna. *The Voice of Authority, 10 Communication Strategies Every Leader Needs to Know.* The McGraw-Hill Companies, 2007.

Booher, Dianna. *Communicate with Confidence: How to Say it Right the First Time and Every Time.* Made for Success, 2011.

Eikenberry, Kevin. *Remarkable Leadership.* Jossey-Bass, 2007.

Additional Notes

8
What is My Role as Coach?

In your role as a supervisor, you will have the responsibility of coaching your team members. Many skills are required to be a successful coach. What you believe about your role as coach will influence what skills you will need to develop and what actions you will need to take.

Activity 1: Responsibilities of a Coach

① Using the table on the following page, check the responsibilities you feel you need as a coach and rank each item in importance on a scale of 1–10 (with 10 being very important).

② Place an asterisk by those responsibilities which you feel confident in completing.

I Need (Check all that apply)	Responsibilities of a Coach	Importance (Ranked 1–10)
	Training on skills	
	Listening to concerns	
	Setting goals and objectives	
	Communicating expectations	
	Providing positive feedback	
	Outlining instructions	
	Giving corrective feedback	
	Reviewing performance	
	Providing resources	
	Modeling behaviors	
	Believing in potential	
	Counseling on behaviors	
	Delegating assignments	
	Supporting career growth	
	Answering questions	
	Asking questions	
	Recognizing interests	
	Removing obstacles	
	Disciplining when necessary	
	Holding others accountable	
	Motivating individuals	
	Encouraging risks	
	Praising and rewarding	
	Communicating instructions	

3 Describe how your current skills will assist you in fulfilling these responsibilities.

4 Put a check mark by the skills that you will need to develop.

5 Plan and record the actions needed to develop those skills.

6 Identify the resources you will use to develop the skills you need.

Activity 2: Walking Through the Coaching Model

This tool will help you plan for using the coaching model, especially as you are getting started. (See the graphic on page 35.) Use this as your planning tool. A template is available by registering at the Bud to Boss Community at **www.budtobosscommunity.com/my-journey-registration/**

❶ Plan a coaching conversation with one of your team members.

❷ What goals do you have for the coaching conversation?

❸ What will you say and ask in the opening steps of the model?

Identifying Expectations:

Defining Impact:

❹ What type of responses do you expect?

5 Think about the plan the team member needs to implement. Prepare your thoughts, but make sure they create the final plan.

6 Determine how you will confirm their commitment to the plan.

After the Coaching Session:

1 Reflect back on the coaching conversation and consider the questions below:

Question	Yes	No
Did you follow your plan?		
Were your questions/comments understood?		
Did your questions/comments obtain the information you needed?		
Was your team member able to respond to your questions?		
Did you control your emotions during the conversation?		
Were you able to influence the person in the desired direction?		
Did your questions assist your team member in coming up with a solution or action plan?		
Did you gain their commitment to the plan?		

② Did you talk more than 50% of the time? (If so, it is very likely that you *talked too much!*)

③ What will you do differently in your next coaching conversation?

③ Follow up with the team member to determine if the actions have improved or corrected the issue/problem.

YOUR **NEXT** STEPS

① Ask your team members to evaluate your coaching skills when you conduct an end-of-the-year performance review with them.

② Consider the Remarkable Coaching Workshop (**www.RemarkableCoaching.com**) as the next step in your development.

③ Read books on coaching, including those suggested below.

④ Ask your supervisor or mentor to sit in on a coaching session and give you feedback on your process and skills (if appropriate).

Suggested Reading

Bell, Chip and Marshall Goldsmith. *Managers as Mentors: Building Partnerships for Learning.* Berrett-Koehler Publishers, Inc., Third edition, 2013.

Eikenberry, Kevin. *Remarkable Leadership.* Jossey-Bass, 2007.

Isaacs, William. *Dialogue: The Art of Thinking Together.* Crown Business, 1999.

Kaye, Beverly and Julie Winkle Guilioni. *Help Them Grow or Watch Them Go: Career Conversations Employees Want.* Berrett-Koehler Publishers, Inc., 2012.

Kaye, Beverly and Sharon Jordan-Evans. *Love 'Em or Lose 'Em: Getting Good People to Stay.* Berrett-Koehler Publishers, Inc., Fifth edition, 2014.

Maruska, Don and Jay Perry. *Take Charge of Your Talent.* Berrett-Koehler Publishers, Inc., 2013.

Zenger, John H. and Kathleen Stinnett. *The Extraordinary Coach: How the Best Leaders Help Others Grow.* The McGraw-Hill Companies, 2010.

Additional Notes

More Notes

9
How Do I Give Feedback?

When you reviewed your role as coach on page 74, you probably checked providing positive and corrective feedback to your team members as essential. In the Bud to Boss Workshop and/or the book *From Bud to Boss,* you learned that there are four basic types of feedback.

Here is a quick review:

Negative Feedback: Comments about past performance that did not go well.

Positive Feedback: Comments about past performance that did go well.

Negative Feedforward: Advice about things to not do in the future.

Positive Feedforward: Advice about what to keep doing or start doing that will lead to better results.

YOUR **NOW** STEPS

Activity 1: Your Feedback Plan

In your role as supervisor, consider the following:

❶ How will you ensure that you provide regular feedback to each member of your team?

❷ How often do you feel you should provide feedback?

❸ What will you do to ensure that you are providing adequate amounts of positive feedback and feedforward to each member of your team?

Activity 2: Specific Feedback

Using the table on the following page, consider the performance of each individual. You can download a digital copy of this form by registering for the Bud to Boss Community at:
www.budtobosscommunity.com/my-journey-registration/

❶ List each team member in the first column.

❷ Positive Behaviors: Identify at least two behaviors where positive feedback/praise is warranted.

❸ Areas for Improvement: Identify any areas which require negative feedback or negative feedforward.

❹ Specifics: List specific things that need to be addressed with each team member.

❺ Opening Statement: Determine your opening statement for introducing the topic to the team member.

❻ Support: Describe the examples or documentation you have which will support what you need to discuss.

❼ Possible Reaction: How is the team member likely to react to feedback? Plan your response.

1 Team Members	**2** Positive Behaviors	**3** Areas for Improvement	**4** Specifics	**5** Opening Statement	**6** Support	**7** Possible Reaction

❶ Give yourself a deadline to complete the discussion with each team member.

❷ Evaluate each of the feedback conversations and determine what you need to do to improve their impact.

❸ Ask your team members to evaluate you on how you provide feedback during the annual performance review process.

Suggested Reading

Blanchard, Ken, and Thad Lacinek, Chuck Tompkins and Jim Ballard. *Whale Done: The Power of Positive Relationships*. Free Press, 2002.

Bruce, Ann. *Perfect Phrases for Documenting Employee Performance Problems*. The McGraw-Hill Companies, 2005.

Eikenberry, Kevin. *Remarkable Leadership*. Jossey-Bass, 2007.

Falcone, Paul. *2600 Phrases for Effective Performance Reviews*. AMA-COM, 2005.

Tulgan, Bruce. *FAST Feedback*. Human Resource Development Press, 2011.

Additional Notes

10
How Do I Handle Change?

It should be obvious to you by now that many things about your work life will change as a result of your transition to supervisor. In the section "How Different Will It Be?" (page 19), you completed some exercises about specific things that will be different in your tasks and responsibilities, roles and relationships, attitudes and beliefs, and your accountabilities.

This section will discuss how you handle change in general rather than specific aspects of your life that will change.

Activity 1: Your Experience with Change

❶ Consider the changes you have made in your life:

✏ Which changes brought about positive results?

✏ What were your feelings about these changes before they occurred?

✎ What actions did you take to make these changes positive?

❷ How can you use this experience and reflection to help lead change for others more successfully?

❸ How can you apply what you have learned in previous experiences to current change efforts?

❹ Think about how you can use your experiences to make future changes more comfortable and successful.

YOUR NEXT STEPS

❶ Think about an upcoming change. As you consider this change, remember the Change Formula you learned in *From Bud to Boss* and in the From Bud to Boss Workshop.

$$D \times V \times Fs > Cp$$

Where...
D = Dissatisfaction with Present Situations
V = Vision of a Better Future
Fs = Clarity of First Steps
Cp = Perceived Cost(s)

❷ Consider these questions:

✐ What is your dissatisfaction with the current situation?

✐ What is your vision of the future that will result from the change?

✏ What are the first steps needed to move this change forward?

✏ What action steps will you take to complete the change?

✏ Who can assist you in this change effort?

✏ What are the risks (perceived costs) you see in implementing this change?

Suggested Reading

Adams, Marilee G. *Change Your Questions, Change Your Life: 10 Powerful Tools for Life and Work*. Berrett-Koehler Publishers, Inc., 2009.

Eikenberry, Kevin. *Remarkable Leadership*. Jossey-Bass, 2007.

Johnson, Spencer. *Who Moved My Cheese?* Penguin Group, 1998.

Maurer, Rick. *Beyond the Wall of Resistance, Why 70% of all Changes Fail and What You Can Do About It*. Bard Press, Texas, 2010.

Petterson, Kerry, and Joseph Grenny, David Maxfield, Ron McMillan, and Al Switzler. *Change Anything: The New Science of Personal Success*. Grand Central Publishing, 2011.

Additional Notes

More Notes

11

How Do I Help Others Handle Change?

You will be responsible for making changes in your department and for introducing changes being implemented by your company to your department. This section will help you think about your role in helping others choose change.

Implementing Change Successfully

1 Identify a change that you must introduce to and implement with your team.

2 Identify possible areas of dissatisfaction with the current state that your team may see or feel. Make a list of questions to help them identify their dissatisfaction.

❸ Create a list of first steps for this change implementation. Make a list of questions to help the team determine these steps.

❹ Plan to understand any resistance you will encounter.

    ✎ What do you think is the source of this resistance?

    ✎ What questions will you ask to uncover/understand the cause of the resistance and risks people see in the change?

✏ What information can you provide or actions can you take that may help alleviate issues and concerns related to the change?

5 Schedule a meeting with your team. Think about how you are going to open the meeting and set up the discussion about the change.

6 Involve your team in creating a vision for the change, determining areas of dissatisfaction, and identifying first steps.

7 Collectively build an action plan for implementing the change. Record it and make sure everyone has a copy.

8 Schedule follow-up meetings to track and advance the change initiative.

Reflect on a Past Change Effort

1 How did the change process work with your team?

❷ What areas were difficult and what went well?

❸ What could you do differently with your next change effort?

❹ Consider how your role impacted the change effort:

   ✎ Did you manage, lead, or champion the change (or how much of each?)

✎ How effective were you?

Suggested Reading

Adams, Marilee G. *Change Your Questions, Change Your Life: 10 Powerful Tools for Life and Work.* Berrett-Koehler Publishers, Inc., 2009.

Eikenberry, Kevin. *Remarkable Leadership.* Jossey-Bass, 2007.

Heath, Chip and Dan Heath. *Switch: How to Change Things When Change is Hard.* Crown Business, 2010

Johnson, Spencer. *Who Moved My Cheese?* Penguin Group, 1998.

Maurer, Rick. *Beyond the Wall of Resistance, Why 70% of all Changes Fail and What You Can Do About It.* Bard Press, Texas, 2010.

Petterson, Kerry, and Joseph Grenny, David Maxfield, Ron McMillan, and Al Switzler. *Influencer: The Power to Change Anything.* The McGraw-Hill Companies, 2007.

Additional Notes

12

How Do I Build My Team?

You have either taken over the supervision of an established team or have been assigned to a new team. You may have been part of this team prior to being supervisor, have come from another part of the organization, or have come from outside. Regardless of which of these apply, you are now responsible for assisting a group of individuals to come together to work toward common goals.

When you read the *From Bud to Boss* book or attended the Bud to Boss Workshop, you learned about the stages of team development. Here's a quick review:

Forming:	*The transition from individual to team.* Team members are anxious; people don't know each other well; tasks and roles are not clear; and tension may be noticed.
Storming:	*The first signs of conflict.* Behaviors are misunderstood and misinterpreted; procedures are being learned; and simple disagreements may surface.
Norming:	*The cohesiveness begins.* Unity and team identity develop; members are involved and more satisfied; and cooperation and collaboration replace conflict.
Performing:	*The goal.* Team members are focused on the goals; members understand and are loyal to each other; members are clear on their roles; and high quality work is accomplished.

Regardless of which stage the team was in when you became the supervisor, because of the dynamic created by adding a new leader, the team is now in the forming stage. (If you have been in place awhile, your team may be in a different stage.)

YOUR **NOW** STEPS

Activity 1: Our Stage of Team Development

1 Consider the dynamics of your team when you became supervisor:

☞ What did you do/can you do to help your team progress through the forming stage more rapidly?

☞ How can you help team members get to know you and each other better?

☞ How can you help team members clarify and understand their team roles and responsibilities?

Activity 2: Moving Through Storming

Once a team moves through forming (which is likely happening after you join as a new leader/member) there will be a stop in the Storming stage. While work can get done during Storming (and many teams stay here a long time), work is hard, frustrating, slow and stressful. This activity will set the stage to help you move your team through Storming, or remove impediments and help them move through it faster.

Start by planning a meeting for your team that isn't about the work or project progress, but about the dynamics of the team. Note – if you have resources to use a neutral facilitator to help you with this process, do so – but don't let that keep you from doing this, even if you have to facilitate.

Before the Meeting:

1 Cement the goal of this meeting in your mind – to work on group process, (and move through Storming), not work on the group's work.

2 Send an agenda describing your goals for this meeting.

3 Think through the questions you want to ask/topics to discuss during this meeting. They could include:

- ✏ Getting clear agreement on the team's goals (and determining where there are differences)

- ✏ Getting clear agreements on roles of team members – both formal and informal.

- ✏ Identifying areas of team agreement to reduce frustration, stress and conflict.

During the Meeting:

1 Start by reviewing the goals and agenda.

2 Let people know that the goal isn't blame but team improvement in productivity and success.

3 Allow people to voice their concerns and move towards agreements for future behaviors of the team.

4 Take notes.

After the Meeting:

1 Get feedback from individuals on the agreements.

2 Hold people accountable for the agreements.

3 Remind people of the purpose – to improve team productivity and reduce frustration.

Activity 3: Planning Meetings

Whatever your team's stage of development, you will have meetings! Meetings are often the best way to communicate, solve problems and make decisions. Unfortunately too many meetings are poorly executed, and much of those problems can be prevented with more effective meeting planning and preparation. To be the best leader you can be, and to help move your team more quickly through the stages of development towards Performing, you need to plan and prepare for meetings more effectively. This activity will help you do this.

❶ Plan a team meeting that needs to occur.

☞ What is the purpose of the meeting? Does this purpose require a meeting? **If not, stop now!**

☞ What needs to happen to reach that purpose? (Create an agenda.)

☞ Who needs to attend the meeting in order for you to meet the purpose/obtain the results required?

✏ When will you send the agenda to participants?

✏ What assignments/information should the participants bring to the meeting?

✏ What meeting roles (note taker, time keeper, etc.) will you assign to meeting participants?

✏ What ground rules will be established for the meeting? Involve the meeting participants in creating the ground rules.

✏ What specific outcomes are you looking for with this meeting?

☞ How will you record the specific action items that result from the meeting?

❷ Schedule the meeting and distribute the agenda.

❸ After the meeting, evaluate the results. Consider the following:

☞ Was the purpose of the meeting met?		Yes	No
☞ Did the meeting follow the agenda?		Yes	No
☞ Were the ground rules followed?		Yes	No
☞ Were action items identified and assigned?		Yes	No

❹ Reflect on the meeting. Determine what went well (and you want to repeat) and what could have been more effective if it had been done differently.

❺ Plan what actions you will take to make the next meeting more effective.

❶ Teach your team the stages of team development.

❷ Ask for their input on how the team can go through the stages the next time there is a change in team membership or goals.

❸ Ask your team to provide feedback/give input on how the team meetings are conducted or ask them to complete a questionnaire on the meetings held.

❹ Make adjustments in how meetings are held based upon their recommendations.

Suggested Reading

Blanchard, Ken, and Alan Randolph and Peter Grazier. *Go Team: Take Your Team to the Next Level.* Berrett-Koehler Publishers, Inc., 2007.

Eikenberry, Kevin. *Remarkable Leadership.* Jossey-Bass, 2007.

Lencioni, Patrick. *The Five Dysfunctions of a Team.* John Wiley & Sons, 2002.

Maxwell, John C. *The 17 Indisputable Laws of Teamwork: Embrace and Empower Your Team.* Thomas Nelson, Inc., 2013.

Additional Notes

13

How Do I Resolve Conflict?

When people work together, they don't always get along. This is a natural result of the differences among people. It is the reaction to and handling of these differences that will determine if the "conflict" will have a positive result or be detrimental to the team.

As a leader/supervisor, you are responsible for more than your personal conflicts. You may need to assist in resolving conflicts between your team members, your team members and employees from other areas of the company, your team members and customers or vendors, or other situations.

You need to be comfortable with conflict resolution as this skill can make you a more effective leader.

YOUR **NOW**  STEPS

Activity 1: Current Conflict in Your Organization

❶ List the conflicts that occur in your work team.

✐ Using the guidelines defined in *From Bud to Boss*, how would you classify these conflicts:

Level 1: Everyday stuff

Level 2: Uncomfortable situations

Level 3: Beyond normal skills

Level 4: Formal processes

Level 5: Intractable

✎ What are the most important issues?

✎ Why do you think the people involved feel threatened?

✎ What is making the people involved feel anger?

❷ Describe what, if anything, you have done to resolve these conflicts.

❸ How successful have your efforts been?

4 What could you have done differently to resolve the situation more effectively?

5 What have you learned about resolving conflicts through these efforts?

YOUR **NEXT** STEPS

1 Describe a conflict which is occurring on your team.

2 Identify the business need/function that is being impacted as a result of this conflict.

❸ Who is involved in the conflict?

❹ List the specific things that you know about the situation.

❺ Develop a plan for addressing the conflict:

   ✍ Determine an appropriate time for a meeting. Be sure to involve
      the team members in setting up the meeting time.

   ✍ Plan your opening statement to introduce the meeting and to
      state your goals for the resolution meeting. Write out your inten-
      tion here. Keep the focus on the business problem caused by the
      conflict.

   ✍ What ground rules will you establish for the interaction?

☞ Describe the process you will use to assist the team members to explain the situation to you and to each other.

☞ Identify the key words you will listen for that will indicate progress is being made with the resolution. Look for indications of vulnerability such as: apologizing, taking responsibility, conceding, self-disclosing, expressing positive emotions, etc.

☞ How will you obtain agreement on and commitment to a solution?

6 Schedule a meeting with the team members involved to follow up on the agreements reached during the first meeting.

Suggested Reading

Dana, Daniel. *Conflict Resolution.* The McGraw-Hill Companies, 2001.

Eikenberry, Kevin. *Remarkable Leadership.* Jossey-Bass, 2007.

Petterson, Kerry, and Joseph Grenny, Ron McMillan, and Al Switzler. *Crucial Conversations: Tools for Talking When Stakes Are High.* The McGraw-Hill Companies, 2011.

Runde, Craig E., and Tim A. Flanagan. *Becoming a Conflict Competent Leader.* John Wiley & Sons, 2007.

Scott, Susan. *Fierce Conversations: Achieving Success at Work and in Life, One Conversation at a Time.* Penguin Group Incorporated, 2004.

Additional Notes

14
What Are My Goals?

Your promotion is likely a sign of reaching one of your goals. People in leadership roles are nearly always continuous learners and high achievers. If that describes you, then you have many more goals that you would like to achieve—in your current job, in your career, and in your personal life. Note: A template to help you with each of the goal-setting activities that follow can be downloaded after registering for the Bud to Boss Community at **www.budtobosscommunity.com/my-journey-registration/**

Activity 1: Department Goals

1 Identify your department goals for your first year as a supervisor:

Area	Goals

2 Determine the specific action steps you will take to obtain each goal. What will you do to ensure continuous effort toward the accomplishment of each goal?

3 Identify the obstacles that may impact your reaching each goal.

4 List the resources you will need or that you can use to help you reach each goal.

5 Describe how you will determine when each goal has been achieved.

6 Discuss these goals with your supervisor.

7 Ensure that your goals are aligned with the goals of your department and your organization.

Activity 2: Relationship Goals

1 Identify your relationship goals for your first year as a supervisor:

Area	Goals

2 Determine the specific action steps you will take to obtain each goal. What will you do to ensure continuous effort toward the accomplishment of each goal?

3 Identify the obstacles that may impact your reaching each goal.

4 List the resources you will need or that you can use to help you reach each goal.

5 Describe how you will determine when each goal has been achieved.

Activity 3: Developmental Goals

1 Identify your developmental goals for your first year as a supervisor:

Area	Goals

2 Determine the specific action steps you will take to obtain each goal. What will you do to ensure continuous effort toward the accomplishment of each goal?

3 Identify the obstacles that may impact your reaching each goal.

4 List the resources you will need or that you can use to help you reach each goal.

5 Describe how you will determine when each goal has been achieved.

Activity 4: Other Goals

❶ Identify your other goals for your first year as a supervisor:

Area	Goals

❷ Determine the specific action steps you will take to obtain each goal. What will you do to ensure continuous effort toward the accomplishment of each goal?

❸ Identify the obstacles that may impact your reaching each goal.

❹ List the resources you will need or that you can use to help you reach each goal.

❺ Describe how you will determine when each goal has been achieved.

❶ Reflect upon your career goals for the next three years and list them here:

❷ Choose those which you consider to be the highest priority.

❸ Determine the specific actions you will have to take to obtain these goals.

❹ Consider the obstacles you feel you may have that will impact your goal achievement.

❺ Assign milestones and deadlines to these goals.

❻ Explain how you will ensure your commitment to accomplishing these goals.

Suggested Reading

Blanchard, Ken and Mark Miller. *Great Leaders GROW: Becoming a Leader for Life*. Berrett-Koehler Publishers, Inc. 2012.

Eikenberry, Kevin. *Remarkable Leadership*. Jossey-Bass, 2007.

Smith, Hyrum. *What Matters Most: The Power of Living Your Values*. Free Press, 2001.

Tracy, Brian. *Goals*. Berrett-Koehler Publishers, Inc., 2010.

Ziglar, Zig and curated by Seth Godin. *Pick Four*. The Domino Project, 2011.

Additional Notes

15
How Do I Set Goals for Others?

As a supervisor, you are responsible not only for your individual goals but also for the goals of your department or team. Since those goals must be accomplished with and through others, you are responsible for assisting your team members to set their goals.

In order for the individual goals to come together to achieve the team goals, individual goals must be aligned with the department/team goals. It should be evident, then, that the department/team goals need to be aligned with the overall goals of the organization.

You may find that in addition to the goals your team members need to accomplish to meet department goals that they may have career/professional development goals that may or may not be designed to keep them in your department or even with the company. As their supervisor, help them to identify and achieve these goals as well.

YOUR **NOW** STEPS

Activity 1: Determining Team Goals

(This activity applies if you are taking over an established team.)

❶ List (or identify if you are not aware) the goals that already have been established for your team.

2 How are the goals aligned with the goals of the department and the organization?

3 Determine if these goals have been effectively communicated to your team members. (In other words, do they know and understand them?)

4 If the goals are unknown or unclear, communicate them to the team.

5 If they are known and clear, assess goal progress to date.

Activity 2: Setting Team Goals

(This applies if goals have not been set for the team or it is the beginning of a new year or goal period.)

1 Find out what the departmental/organizational goals are for the applicable time period. List those here.

2 Meet with your team and discuss the following:

  ✏ Communicate these higher level goals.

  ✏ Discuss and identify the goals the team should set to help the department/organization reach its goals.

✏ Be sure that the goals meet the SMART criteria (Specific, Measurable, Action-Oriented, Realistic, and Time-Dimensioned).

✏ Determine which goals have the highest priority. Why?

✏ Identify the action steps to achieve these goals.

✏ Determine who will be responsible for each action step.

❸ After the meeting, prepare a document outlining the goals and share it with all team members.

❹ Periodically follow-up with the team to discuss progress toward the goals.

❺ Determine how the team will be rewarded (or will reward themselves) when the goals are achieved.

Activity 3: Setting Individual Goals

❶ What is the process you will use to set goals with your individual team members?

❷ Discuss and select goals appropriate for each team member and the time period needed to achieve the goals. Use the table on the following page to prepare your thinking for the conversations. You can download a digital copy of this form by registering for the Bud to Boss Community at **www.budtobosscommunity.com/my-journey-registration/**

☞ Column 1: List each of your team members.

☞ Column 2: Identify goals appropriate for each one.

☞ Column 3: Specify the time period needed to achieve each goal.

1. Team Member	2. Goals	3. Time Period

3 Ensure that the individual goals are aligned with the team goals.

4 Be sure that the goals meet the SMART criteria (Specific, Measurable, Action-Oriented, Realistic, and Time Dimensioned).

5 Determine action steps that will ensure progress towards the goals. Establish milestones or deadlines for the action steps.

YOUR **NEXT** STEPS

1 Prepare a document outlining the goals and make sure both of you have a copy. Include as a part of your performance management process as appropriate.

2 Establish a process and schedule for following up on the progress toward the goals.

3 Discuss with each team member appropriate rewards or recognition for goal achievement.

Suggested Reading

Blanchard, Ken and Mark Miller. *The Secret: What Great Leaders Know and Do.* Berrett-Koehler Publishers, Inc., 2009.

Eikenberry, Kevin. *Remarkable Leadership.* Jossey-Bass, 2007.

Kaye, Beverly and Julie Winkle Guilioni. *Help Them Grow or Watch Them Go: Career Conversations Employees Want.* Berrett-Koehler Publishers, Inc., 2012.

Maxwell, John C. *Developing the Leaders Around You.* Thomas Nelson, Inc., 2005.

Smith, Hyrum. *What Matters Most: The Power of Living Your Values.* Free Press, 2001.

Tracy, Brian. *Goals.* Berrett-Koehler Publishers, Inc., 2010.

Additional Notes

More Notes

16
Additional Resources for Your Success

The Kevin Eikenberry Group offers world-class training and resources designed specifically for the transition from being an individual contributor to a leader! The products and services listed here are just a small sampling of what we can offer to you and the new leaders in your organization, so please contact us if you have a specific question or other training and learning needs. We pride ourselves on being Your Leadership Help Button and we look forward to serving you!

Introducing...The Bud to Boss Toolkit® —
20 e-Learning Courses to Ease the Transition

The **Bud to Boss Toolkit** is designed specifically to address the needs of anyone who is new to supervising and managing others and is the perfect next-step to develop your learning beyond this book.

In partnership with...

The sad truth is that 40% of new managers fail within the first 18 months of their promotion, because they don't get the training they need to deal with people, manage workloads, mediate conflict, juggle deadlines and much more. **The Bud to Boss Toolkit is just one more resource to ensure that you don't become a statistic!**

e-Learning Course List

#1100m: Discussing Your New Leadership Role

#1105m: Understand the Expectations of a New Role

#1110m: Creating the Mindset for Your New Role

#1115m: Control vs. Influence

#1120m: Communicating Positive Expectations

#1125m: Motivation for Change

#1130m: Accelerate the Acceptance of Organizational Change

#1135m: Diagnose Resistance to Change

#1140m: Dominant Communication Style

#1145m: Inspiring Communication Style

#1150m: Supportive Communication Style

#1155m: Cautious Communication Style

#1160m: Seven Components of Great Presentations

#1165m: Sources of Feedback

#1170m: Four Types of Feedback

#1175m: Six-Step Coaching Model

#1180m: Remove Yourself as a Source of Threat

#1185m: Creating a Conflict Resolution Mindset

#1190m: Accelerate Goal Achievement

#1195m: Goal Setting at Three Levels

Visit http://budtoboss.com/elearning to learn more and request information!

7 Reasons Why New Supervisor Training Is Essential

- Are you hiring or promoting more supervisors because of business growth?

- Do you require new supervisors due to retirements or promotion of other leaders?

- Or do you need more new supervisors due to other sorts of turnover?

There are plenty of reasons you may find yourself with new leaders in your organization. And one of the most powerful investments your organization can make now is in training to help make them more successful!

We have recently released a powerful special report, *7 Reasons Why New Supervisor Training Is Essential*, and we would like to share this with you.

This special report is meant to help you understand the massive impact these supervisors will have on the short- and long-term results of your organization and why time spent in helping them to be more successful could be one of the most powerful investments your organization could make now.

We'll share seven major reasons why this investment is required—and will help you sell that proposition to others in your organization.

SPECIAL REPORT:

7 Reasons Why New Supervisor Training Is Essential

By Kevin Eikenberry

We want to help you, your new leaders, and your organization to be successful—and this is one way we hope to do exactly that.

Visit **www.budtoboss.com/7-things-for-new-supervisors-free-report/** to learn more and get your free copy!

Tell Your Colleagues about the Bud to Boss Workshop!

The Bud to Boss workshop is a powerful, interactive, 2-day event where new supervisors can get the professional foundation they need to succeed and learn how to:

- Influence, work and negotiate with people—not just boss them around.

- Mediate and negotiate.

- Get rid of the fear of conflict by learning ways to address it and neutralize it.

- Engage, lead and develop a team.

- Manage time and juggle an ever-changing list of priorities.

- Improve communication to be more powerful, persuasive and memorable.

- Overcome resistance and accelerate organizational change.

- Delegate effectively to increase productivity and motivation.

- Implement an effective coaching model that maximizes their team's performance.

Here's what is included with registration:

- ✓ 3 live, group coaching sessions after the workshop to answer any questions that pop up after the return to the office and to help solidify what was learned in the class

- ✓ A free copy of *From Bud to Boss: Secrets to a Successful Transition to Remarkable Leadership* – the new leader's indispensable guide for how to achieve immediate and ongoing success in leadership

- ✓ A 6-month subscription to *The Insider* – our print newsletter filled with the latest ideas and new applications of timeless leadership principle written for leaders

 And every registration is backed with our 100% Satisfaction Guarantee! We believe our work isn't done until you are completely satisfied with the results you have received from our training. When you choose to learn with us, if, for any reason you aren't 100% delighted with the workshop, we will refund your entire registration fee. No questions asked. Guaranteed.

Check **www.BudtoBoss.com** for a complete list of upcoming dates and locations!

Have more than a few new supervisors/leaders to help improve? We can bring the Bud to Boss Workshop to YOUR organization!

With our unique, customized, on-site training program, you can train employees at the location of your choice and customize the program to meet your objectives.

Why choose on-site training?

✓ Customization: Our standard workshops are available across the United States, but on-site training can be tailored to fit YOUR organization's unique needs and YOUR challenges. Our trainer will work with you to use your language and meet your specific needs.

✓ Convenience: You choose the time, duration, and location that are convenient for you and your employees.

✓ Cost: By bringing the training to your location, you realize significant savings on a per-employee basis, eliminate travel expenses, and reduce the time out of the office.

Remember – our experienced training consultants will work with you individually to create the right training solution for you.

To learn more about this option and to schedule time to talk to one of our learning concierges, visit **www.BudtoBoss.com**.

Have a big organizational need for new supervisor training?

The need for more competent and confident new supervisors has never been higher – and you realize this need. Up until now you could send your folks to one of our public workshops, or hire us to bring one of our master trainers to your site to deliver these skills to your leaders.

Now, you have a third option.

Now you can have world-class training, licensed in your organization, by certifying your trainers in the proven From-Bud-to-Boss content.

Certification and licensing is for you if . . .

✓ You have a pent-up need for new supervisor training.

✓ You have a new leader workshop – and it focuses on the laws and policies – but you know you need the leadership piece too.

✓ You have a steady stream of new supervisors coming on board due to fast growth or a changing business environment.

✓ You have talented trainers.

✓ You don't have time to build your own program and see no reason to re-invent the wheel.

✓ You want the credibility that comes with partnering with the best-selling book on new supervisor and leader success.

As a certified and licensed Bud to Boss training provider, here is what you get in your certification experience:

✓ A 4.5-day, interactive, advanced learning experience preparing a trainer to successfully deliver the material—trainers leave certified to use and deploy this training. You are guaranteed to have at least one of the authors and course designers, Kevin Eikenberry or Guy Harris, as one of your trainers – and maybe both!

✓ Special certified-trainer dinner with Kevin and his team.

✓ Access to and use of video support for the training (authors Kevin and Guy teaching critical pieces of the content for maximum success).

✓ 1 hour of personal coaching prior to your first training session.

✓ Access to additional materials.

✓ Ability to purchase workshop materials—not available anywhere, unless you are certified and licensed.

✓ Discounts on the *From Bud to Boss* book and the *My Journey from Bud to Boss* learning journal—to make your training more powerful for your participants.

Trainer-certification investments start at $3,000 for the complete experience. Whether you need 1 or 50 trainers, contact us today!

Contact Barb McLin at 888.LEARNER ext. 4 or go to **www.BudtoBoss.com** to learn more.

Invest in Yourself, Invest in Your Skills with These Additional Training Opportunities!

KevinEikenberry.com/Remote

This unique series is small group experience delivered remotely. It is 7 online sessions targeted for the skills a remote leader needs, including building a virtual team, leading virtual meetings, presenting effectively over the web, coaching from a distance and much more.

RemarkableCoaching.com

This workshop starts by covering a practical coaching model and then goes beyond coaching – you'll prepare an action plan to help you become a more effective coach right away and over the long term.

RemarkableLeadership.com

This workshop is essential for any leadership journey. You'll gain practical and actionable tools & skills to help master the competencies of effective leadership.

RemarkableCommunicator.com/ Conflict-Confidence

This isn't just another conflict management training course. It first focuses on understanding conflict –diagnosing each type of conflict to help better choose the right resolution strategy. You'll learn proactive strategies to start confidently handling conflict & confrontation.

RemarkableCommunicator.com

This interactive and powerful workshop is designed to provide leaders with the essential communication skills to influence and persuade and ultimately get greater productivity and results.

More Leadership & Learning Resources
That You Might Find Helpful

Kevin's Leadership and Learning Blog: This is the home of Kevin's ongoing thoughts, ideas, and tools to help you in a variety of professional areas. It includes continually updated thoughts on Customer Service, Creativity, Leadership, Learning, Teamwork, and Training.
Learn more here: **Blog.KevinEikenberry.com**

The Recovering Engineer Blog: This is where you can find Guy's thoughts, insights, and tips for communicating more effectively, resolving conflicts more quickly, and building better personal and professional relationships.
Learn more here: **RecoveringEngineer.com**

Sara Jane Hope's Website and Blog: Sara Jane maintains a leadership blog and provides information about the many training services with her company, Positive Dimensions, on her website. Look for her first book, *Coached by the Captain.*
Learn more here: **SaraJaneHope.com**

20 Days to Remarkable Leadership: A free, video training course with 14 training videos and companion learning tools, giving you inspiration, ideas and a bit-by-bit way to learn critical leadership skills (plus free gifts and some cool bonuses too).
Learn more here: **KevinEikenberry.com/20-Days**

Unleashing Your Remarkable Potential: Kevin's weekly e-newsletter with valuable leadership lessons and resource recommendations delivered every Monday morning.
Learn more here: **KevinEikenberry.com/unleashing-your-remarkable-potential/**

DISC Personality Testing: If you are looking for a quick tool to help you apply the communication, motivation, and coaching concepts in this journal, our DISC Personality Test is just what you need. You can get a quick DISC Assessment for an instant estimate of your DISC profile based on answers to 12 short questions. If you'd like deeper insights and more application tips, you can purchase the full, 24 question version.
In no more than 10 minutes, you'll have a better understanding of why you communicate the way you do and insights into how you can communicate with others more effectively. With your results, you can:

✓ Immediately improve interpersonal communications

✓ Connect with co-workers more effectively

✓ Understand what you need to do to be more successful in your interactions with others.

Learn more here: DiscPersonalityTesting.com

Remarkable Learning: Presented by top experts in their field, our Remarkable Learning Teleseminars are jam-packed with great information on the issues that matter the most to you and designed specifically so that you don't even have to leave your office. Plus – when you register for a teleseminar, your entire team can train along with you for FREE, because your registration entitles you to unlimited participants per connection! Topics include:

✓ Communication & Interpersonal Skills

✓ Management & Leadership

✓ New Supervisor Training

✓ Coaching & Developing Others

✓ Presentation Skills

✓ Conflict Management & Resolution

✓ Time Management & Organization

Learn more here: **www.RemarkableLearning.com**

About the Authors

Kevin Eikenberry

Kevin Eikenberry is a world-renowned leadership expert, a two-time bestselling author, speaker, consultant, trainer, coach, leader, learner, husband, and father. He is the founder and Chief Potential Officer of The Kevin Eikenberry Group. In 2014 *Inc.com* named him one of the Top 100 Leadership and Management Thinkers in the World.

He has spent the last 25 years helping organizations all across North America, and clients from around the world, on leadership, learning, teams and teamwork, communication and more. His client list is wide and varied both geographically and by industry.

Kevin is a frequent presenter at professional conferences and a sought-after keynote speaker, and his company promotes several leadership and communications workshops around the United States (including workshops on the transition From Bud to Boss!).

He is the author of the bestselling books *Remarkable Leadership: Unleashing Your Leadership Potential One Skill at a Time* and *Vantagepoints on Learning and Life.* He also wrote the unique #Leadershiptweet – a collection of short leadership ideas originally written and published on Twitter and is a contributing author to more than 20 other books. With Guy Harris he also co-authored *From Bud to Boss – Secrets to a Successful Transition to Remarkable Leadership.*

He publishes four electronic newsletters and a blog (Blog.KevinEikenberry.com) collectively read by thousands of people worldwide and consistently listed as one of the Internet's most-read blogs on leadership.

While Kevin lives in Indianapolis, Indiana, part of his heart is always on the farm he grew up on in western Michigan.

Guy Harris

Guy Harris consults, coaches, trains, and writes in the areas of team and interaction dynamics, communication strategies and tactics, and emotional intelligence.

Guy served as a nuclear engineering officer on a U.S. Navy submarine and he worked in leadership positions in business.

Typical client concerns prior to working with him are: helping groups to become teams, moving past conflicts, developing leaders, communicating more effectively, and developing buy-in.

Guy helps clients understand—and work through—relationship dynamics that get in the way of getting things done.

He writes the Recovering Engineer Blog (**http://recoveringengineer.com**). He co-authored *From Bud to Boss: Secrets to a Successful Transition to Remarkable Leadership.*

Guy has degrees in chemical engineering. He is a master trainer and coach in the DISC Model of Human Behavior and a workplace conflict resolution expert.

Sara Jane Hope

Sara Jane Hope, PHR, is an experienced, dedicated, and enthusiastic trainer, facilitator, and coach. Having worked in training since 1980, she is a training and human resources professional dedicated to making a difference in the performance and knowledge of her trainees.

Currently a vice president and corporate training director for a large regional financial institution, she is also is the owner of Positive Dimensions where she provides leadership- and management-development training and coaching.

Sara Jane is a certified master trainer and a Bud to Boss facilitator and coach for the Kevin Eikenberry Group. Sara Jane Hope has a Master's degree from Murray State University and a Bachelor of Arts degree from Purdue University. Originally from a farm in Indiana, she currently lives in Ridgeland, Mississippi, with her husband, Larry, and their dog, Allie. She avidly reads, loves to crochet, and follows many sports teams.

She can be reached at SaraJaneHope.com.

Addendum

This page and the following blank ones are included for when you need additional space for the activities. They will help you keep your notes all together in one place and with this guide.